(WELLINGTON SQUARE)

Danger in the
pond

Tessa Krailing

WELLINGTON SQUARE

Contents

The monster

It was Saturday morning.
Mr Keeping, Tessa and Tony were going
through the park in Wellington Square.
They were going to see what
they could find in the pond.
'Is there a monster in our pond?' asked Tessa.
Tony laughed at her.
But Mr Keeping said, 'Lots of monsters.
I'll show them to you.'
The twins looked surprised.
They weren't sure they wanted to see
lots of monsters.

When they came to the pond, Mr Keeping said,
'Dip your nets into the water and see
what you can find.'
The twins dipped their nets into the pond.
Tony took his net out first but
it was full of weeds.
'My net is full of weeds!' said Tony.
'Take your net out, Tessa,' said Mr Keeping.
Tessa took her net out of the water.
'I've got something!' she shouted.
Mr Keeping told her to put it carefully
into the tray.

They looked into the tray to see what
Tessa had got.
'What is it?' asked Tony.
'That's a Great Diving Beetle,'
said Mr Keeping.
'It will eat small animals like frogs.'
The Great Diving Beetle moved around
the tray, looking for a way to get out.
The twins were watching the beetle but
Mr Keeping was looking in the pond.

He picked something out of the water and
told the twins to come and look at what
he had found.
He had a dead frog in his hand.
The twins saw other dead frogs and
fish in the pond.
'Wow,' said Tony.
'Look at all these dead frogs.'
'And fish,' said Tessa.
'What could have killed them?' asked Tessa.
'It could have been the Great Diving Beetle,'
said Tony.
'I don't think so,' said Mr Keeping.
'I don't think an animal killed them.'
'What then?' asked Tony.

Mr Keeping dipped his hand into the water and
picked up a big can.
'This is what killed the frogs and
the fish,' he said.
'This can of weed killer.
Someone has been putting rubbish
in the pond.
They thought this can of weed killer was
empty but it wasn't.
The animals are in danger.
All this rubbish is killing them.'
Mr Keeping put his hands in the water
again and picked out more rubbish.
'People shouldn't do this!' he said crossly.

As Mr Keeping was cleaning up the pond,
Fred came over to see what was going on.
'Look at this, Fred,' said Tony.
'Look what we've found in the pond.'
Fred saw the pile of rubbish Mr Keeping
had taken out of the water.
'Someone has been putting rubbish
in the pond again!' shouted Fred.
'This has got to stop!
One day I'll catch the monster who
is putting rubbish in my pond.
You see if I don't!'
When Fred had gone, Mr Keeping picked up
the rubbish and Tony carefully put
the Great Diving Beetle back into the pond.
As they went home, the twins talked about
how they could catch the people who were
putting rubbish in the pond.

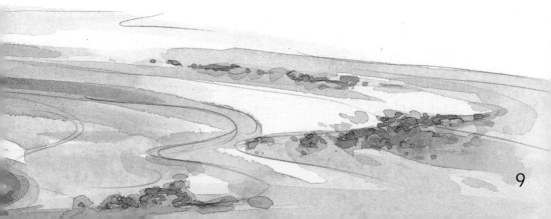

Pond watch

That night, after their Mum and Dad
were in bed, Tessa and Tony got up.
They were going to the pond.
It would be cold outside, so they put on
warm clothes.
'Come on,' said Tessa.
'You take the torch and I'll take the net.
We must find out who is putting rubbish
in the pond.'

It was very dark and the twins were a little
afraid as they left the house.
They made their way across the park and
sat down behind a big tree next to the pond.
The twins looked around.
No-one was about and it was very quiet.
'I'm cold,' said Tessa.
'Me too,' said Tony.
'But we have to do this to save the animals.'

'What's the time?' asked Tessa.
Tony told her to switch on the torch so
that he could look at his watch.
'It's only half-past-ten!' he said.
'Half-past-ten,' said Tessa.
'It must be later than that!'
'My watch is right,' said Tony.
'We've only been here ten minutes.'
'It seems like ten hours!' said Tessa.
'I'm cold and I don't like being out
at night.'

12

'Sh!' said Tony.

'What is it?' asked Tessa.

'There was a strange noise!'

The twins were very quiet and the strange
noise came again.

'Hoo hoo! Hoo hoo!'

'There!' said Tony. 'What was that?'

'Only an owl,' said Tessa.

'Not the monster we are looking for.'

Tony looked at his watch again.

'Eleven o'clock.

If we don't see the monster soon we'll have to ...'

'Sh!' said Tessa. 'Did you hear that?'

'What?' asked Tony.

'Someone is moving about near the pond!'
said Tessa.

The twins looked out from behind
the big tree.

They saw someone near the pond.

'When I say go, we'll jump out,' said Tony.
'Have you got the net?'
'Yes,' said Tessa, as she picked it up.
The twins knew they would have to be quick if
they were going to catch the monster.
'Go!' said Tony.
Tessa and Tony jumped out from behind
the tree.
'I've got him!' shouted Tessa.
'So have I!' shouted Tony.
'We've got the monster who is putting
rubbish in the pond.'
'Let me go!' shouted the man.
'We must tell Fred,' said Tessa.
'I AM Fred!' shouted the man.
'Let me go!'
Tessa switched on the torch and the twins
saw that they had got Fred in the net.

The twins got Fred out of the net.
He was very cross.
'What are you doing here?' he asked.
The twins told him why they were there.
'We were keeping watch on the pond,'
said Tessa.
'We wanted to catch the monster who was
killing the animals with rubbish,' said Tony.
Fred told them that was why he was there too.
'You two must go home,' he said.
'You shouldn't be out at this time of night.
You should be in bed.'
The twins left Fred by the pond and
went home to bed.
They hadn't got the monster and
they had made Fred cross.

Save our pond

Next day Tessa and Tony talked about
the pond.
'What are we going to do?' asked Tessa.
'We can't go to the pond every night.'
Tony thought for a minute.
'I know,' he said.
'We'll make a sign and take it around
the Square.
When people see it they won't put rubbish
in the pond again.'
'Yes,' said Tessa.
'Let's get some paint and make a big sign.'

The twins painted a big sign.
It said, 'Don't put rubbish in the pond.
            Don't kill the animals.'
They went around the Square with the sign.
'Not everyone's seen us,' said Tessa.
'Some people are still at home.'
'Let's go around all the houses,' said Tony.
'Then we can be sure everyone's seen the sign.'

The twins went around all the houses in the Square with the sign.
Mr Miller looked at the sign.
'I think you are right,' he said.
'I don't put rubbish in the pond.
You should take the sign next door.
I'm sure the man there puts his rubbish in the pond.'

Mr Miller went over to the fence.
'Come and see,' he said to the twins.
Tessa and Tony looked over the fence.
A man was clearing his garden.
'At first he put his rubbish in my garden,'
said Mr Miller.
'I told him to take it away and I think he
took it to the pond.
Go and show him your sign.'

Tessa and Tony went to the house next door.
The man looked up.
'Good morning,' said Tessa.
'What do you want?' asked the man.
'We saw that you were clearing your garden,'
said Tony.
'We wanted to show you this sign.'
The man didn't look very pleased.
'Go away!' he said.
'I'll put my rubbish where I want to.
It's got nothing to do with you!'

Tessa and Tony took the sign away.

'I'm sure it's him,' said Tessa.

'He's the monster who is putting rubbish
in the pond.'

'Yes,' said Tony.

'I'm sure it's him too.
Look, he's picking up the rubbish now.
We can follow him and see if he takes it
to the pond.'

'I'm sure he'll take it when it's dark,' said Tessa.

'It'll be dark at eight.
What time is it now?'

Tony looked at his watch.

'Half-past-six,' he said.

'One and a half hours to go.'

Catch the monster!

Tessa and Tony watched the man go
inside his house.
At eight o'clock, when it was getting dark,
he came out again.
The twins saw him pick up the rubbish and
leave the garden.
They followed him quietly.
'He's going to the park,' said Tessa.
'He's taking the rubbish to the park.'
'I'm sure he's going to put it in the
pond,' said Tony.

The man went across the park and
over to the pond.
The twins followed him.
When they reached the pond they watched
him from behind a big tree.
He looked around to make sure no-one was
watching, and quickly put the rubbish
into the pond.
'Look, it IS him! He IS the monster!'
said Tony.
'Yes,' said Tessa.
'He's the monster who is killing the animals
in the pond.'

Just then Fred ran over.

The twins saw that he was very cross.

He was shouting at the man.

'Here, stop that!

Stop putting that rubbish in my pond!'

The man saw Fred coming.

He dropped the rubbish and ran.

The twins jumped out from behind the
tree to stop him.

Fred ran up from behind.

Now the man could not get away.

'What do you want?' shouted the man.
'We want to know if you put a big can of
weed killer into the pond,' said Tony.
'What if I did?' said the man.
'It's killing the animals,' said Tony.
'The can was empty,' said the man.
'No, it wasn't,' said Tessa.
'There was some weed killer left inside it.'
'It killed lots of frogs and fish,'
said Tony.
Fred told the man to clean up the pond and
not to put rubbish in it again.
The man wasn't too pleased, but he picked
up his rubbish and took it home.

'The pond is cleaner now,' said the twins.

'Yes,' said Mr Keeping.

'Now that we've cleaned it and
now that he has taken all his rubbish away.'

'Do you think the pond is safe again for
the frogs and fish?' asked Tessa.

'Let's have a look,' said Mr Keeping.

Mr Keeping looked into the water.

'Come here,' he said to the twins.

'Be very quiet.'

The twins went over quietly and saw
a frog jumping out of the water.

'See,' said Mr Keeping.

'That frog is OK, and the others will
be too, now that the pond is clean again.'